A Guide to

Mývatn

and its surroundings

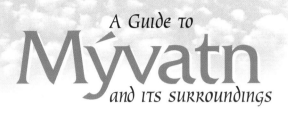

A Guide to
Mývatn
and its surroundings

Helgi Guðmundsson

Design and layout:
Jón Ásgeir í Aðaldal

Forlagið

A Guide to Mývatn and its surroundings
© Helgi Guðmundsson, 2002
English translation © Björg Árnadóttir, Andrew Cauthery, 2002
Illustrations: Jón Ásgeir í Aðaldal, Jón Baldur Hlíðberg
Layout: Jón Ásgeir í Aðaldal
Photographs scanned by: Pixel/Halldór Ólafsson
Printed in Denmark
Published in 2002 by FORLAGIÐ ©, an imprint of
Edda Media & Publishing, Reykjavík, Iceland.

ISBN 9979-53-403-6

Contents

Preface

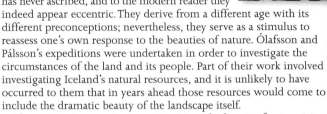

"As we descended the heath, Lake Mývatn and its environs spread out before us, dark and hideous to behold."

With these words from their Travel Journal, Eggert Ólafsson and Bjarni Pálsson described their first impressions of the area around Mývatn, to which they journeyed in the summer of 1752.

Such views are ones to which the present writer has never ascribed, and to the modern reader they indeed appear eccentric. They derive from a different age with its different preconceptions; nevertheless, they serve as a stimulus to reassess one's own response to the beauties of nature. Ólafsson and Pálsson's expeditions were undertaken in order to investigate the circumstances of the land and its people. Part of their work involved investigating Iceland's natural resources, and it is unlikely to have occurred to them that in years ahead those resources would come to include the dramatic beauty of the landscape itself.

I have extensive experience as a tourist guide showing foreign visitors round Iceland, and am therefore familiar with Mývatn as a region absolutely unique in the richness and diversity of its ecosystem. Though my travels in the area have been frequent, they have, with one exception, been during the summer months; my acquaintance with its natural history is, consequently, largely confined to the summer season.

Although much information is available about Mývatn, it seemed to me that a handy reference book would be of some benefit. My aim is to attempt an introduction to the Mývatn area in a concise but accessible manner.

Much has been written about the geology and natural history of Mývatn in recent years, so there was plenty of material to draw from in compiling the present work. I have forged links with many scientists and scholars, and the knowledge of many local inhabitants, generously shared, has been a rich source of information. Responsibility for any inaccuracy is, of course, entirely my own.

I hope that my readers will gain both pleasure and knowledge about the Mývatn area. Should they be spurred on to discover more, my purpose will have been achieved.

Helgi Guðmundsson

LAKE MÝVATN AND ITS SURROUNDINGS

Mývatn is about 50 km from the sea, on the fringes of the highlands of northeast Iceland. The landscape has been moulded by glacial and volcanic activity; since the end of the last Ice Age about 10,000 years ago the whole area has undergone tremendous changes, which are still in progress. As the Ice Age glacier receded it left behind elevations and depressions, including a large, shallow lake in a hollow scoured out by the ice sheet. There will also have been some subsidence. This water-filled basin formed the beginnings of modern Mývatn. The landscape of the period was possibly not unlike that of the present-day desert highlands. Later volcanic activity created natural dams, which trapped the underground water flowing from beneath adjoining layers of lava, and formed the lake proper.

Mývatn is surrounded by geological formations from various periods. To the north of the lake are moraines marking the extent of the ice sheet about 10–11,000 years ago. In the west and southwest there are undulating glacial hills and ridges, and towards the southeast and east there are tuff ridges and cliffs formed during the most recent glacial periods.

Mývatn is on the northern edge of Óðáða-hraun, the collective name for a series of lava fields that form the largest stretch of continuous lava in Iceland, covering an area of nearly 4,500 km². The land inclines in a southerly direction, from about 400 m above sea level in the north to about 1,000 m at its highest in the south, the lava mass reaching at least all the way to the Vatnajökull ice cap. Mountains and mountain

When God Almighty had created heaven and earth he examined his work and saw that it was indeed good. But the devil was not pleased; the beauty of the world irked him, and in his anger he urinated at the sun, meaning to extinguish this crowning glory of creation. But the devil's urine fell short of his purpose, and formed instead Mývatn in the north of Iceland, a lake not only ugly to the eye, but also, with the midges from which it takes its name, truly a torment for both man and beast.

(From the Folk Tales of Jón Árnason)

Herðubreið

ranges rise out of the plateau, the most prominent and best known of these being Herðubreið and Dyngjufjöll. There are many lava-shield mountains (the word for which is *dyngja*) in Ódáðahraun, the largest of these being Trölladyngja and Kollóttadyngja. Ódáðahraun is extremely dry and barren; rainfall is low, and is usually drawn down into the porous lava below, continuing on its way underground and producing the main inflow into Mývatn.

In a nutshell

Aerial view of the Krafla eruption of September 1977.

Geology

The land is relatively young in geological terms. The mountains surrounding Mývatn were mainly formed by volcanic eruptions under the glacier during the most recent Ice Ages. Table mountains of tuff were formed where the magma was able to burst through the glacier; where it could not, it formed ridges. Later periods produced many prominent volcanic cones and crater-rows.

Mývatn is on the western edge of the active volcanic area which straddles Iceland, forming part of the Mid-Atlantic Ridge, a huge belt of volcanic activity that runs up the centre of the Atlantic Ocean and separates the tectonic plates of Eurasia and

The Mid-Atlantic Ridge

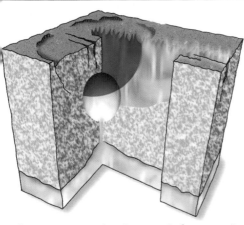

Simplified cross-section of the Mount Krafla area. Under a circa 10 km thick crust lies a mass of partially melted rock from the mantle. Bubbles of magma force their way up and collect under the crust. From there the magma flows towards the magma chamber at a depth of 3 – 7 km under the caldera of the Krafla volcano. The chamber contains two types of magma: at the top basalt magma, perhaps left over from earlier volcanic activity, and below it heavier, more recently formed material. Pressure in the chamber builds up until its walls burst and the magma breaks out, the upper magma forcing a path straight up to the surface, the lower magma going upward and to the sides, following existing fissure swarms.

North America. Here the plates are drifting apart by round two centimetres a year, causing frequent volcanic eruptions.

The bedrock of the Mývatn area is mostly basalt lava and tuff. Within the volcanic area itself are numerous fissures and crater-rows, and in various places wider rifts where the earth's crust has been stretched and torn by the tectonic separation. The fissures are aligned south-southwest to north-northeast, and the volcanic belt with its fissure swarms stretches from the central plateau northwards to the shore of Öxarfjörður.

Volcanic activity takes place in short bursts, often interspersed with long breaks extending over several centuries. Geologists distinguish two to three main phases of vulcanism around Mývatn since the last Ice Age. The first phase is named after the tephra-ring Lúdent, about five kilometres east of the lake, which was probably active shortly after the end of the Ice Age, about 10,000 years ago. The second phase is named after Hverfjall, the

The Krafla eruption of October 18th, 1980.

▲ Hverfjall

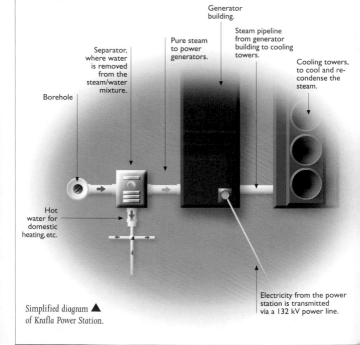

Generator building.

Pure steam to power generators.

Steam pipeline from generator building to cooling towers.

Cooling towers, to cool and re-condense the steam.

Separator, where water is removed from the steam/water mixture.

Borehole

Hot water for domestic heating, etc.

Electricity from the power station is transmitted via a 132 kV power line.

Simplified diagram ▲ of Krafla Power Station.

est known tephra-ring volcano in Iceland and a prominent landmark in the mountain range that encircles Mývatn. Hverfjall was formed about 2,500 years ago in a massive but probably short-lived explosive eruption. Finally there were the so-called Mývatn Eruptions of the first half of the 18th century and the Krafla Eruptions between 1975 and 1984. The 20th-century activity can be considered a continuation of that of the 18th century, and is named after the central crater volcano Krafla, situated about five kilometres northeast of Lake Mývatn.

At the centre of this volcano is a caldera, under which lies a magma chamber at a depth of about three to seven kilometres. As this chamber fills up, the ground level above rises; when it starts to subside, this is an indication that the chamber is emptying and the magma forcing its way to the surface, and therefore that an eruption is imminent. All seismic activity in the area is closely monitored, not least for reasons of safety.

Substantial lava eruptions occurred to the east of Mývatn about 3,800 years ago. At that time a stream of lava from the eruption of Ketildyngja flowed from about 25 km southeast of Lake Mývatn almost all the way to the coast. It was this lava field (known as the Older Laxárhraun) which dammed off the existing Mývatn basin to form a lake roughly of the size we see today.

This process of shaping the modern lake was continued and completed by the Younger Laxárhraun lava field, which originated about 2,000 years ago from the Hlidentsborgir and Þrengslaborgir crater-rows, respectively about five kilometres east and southeast of Lake Mývatn. This lava flowed into the existing lake,

The astronauts who landed on the moon in 1969 had rehearsed their moon-walk in the lava field around Askja, which was considered to resemble the surface of the moon.

The Skútustaðir craters on an Icelandic stamp. These are a good example of pseudo-craters.

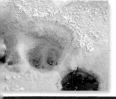

Tourists should take great care in hot-spring areas. Innocuous-looking holes may conceal heat in excess of 100°C. Never allow children into a hot-spring area without supervision.

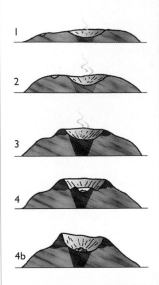

continuing down the Laxárdalur vall[e] all the way to the coast. The valley a[n] the lava fields alike draw their name from the river Laxá, which forms th[e] outflow from Lake Mývatn.

As this lava flowed towards the se[a] it created some of the most unusual natural formations of the Mývatn distri[ct] such as Kálfastrandarstrípar and Dimm[u]borgir, as well as the myriad of pseud[o] craters (over 1,000 of them in all) whi[ch] mark the area and form many of the indentations and islets which so chara[ct]erize the natural beauty of the lake.

During the Mývatn Eruptions of 1724–1729 yet another stream of la[va] ran into the water, this time from th[e] northeast, filling up part of its northe[rn] end. In addition, seismological activ[ity] throughout its existence has caused t[he] bedrock and consequently the botto[m] of Lake Mývatn itself to rise and subsi[de] by turns.

Simplified cross-sections showing how pseudo-craters may have formed in the Lake Mývatn area:
1-2: Steam erupts in many places, and a platform of fine cinder builds up. Steam explosions take place in newly fallen cinder and small pits are formed.
3: Active eruptive vents become fewer, and a rim of coarser cinder is formed on the crater.
4: The eruption is abating. A small crater has formed inside the large crater and finally a spatter cone forms at the centre. It is common for the rim of the crater to be reinforced with splashes of lava (4b).

Pseudo-craters ▶

HYDROLOGY

Lake Mývatn is one of Iceland's largest lakes. A long, narrow spit divides it into two parts linked by a narrow channel – Ytriflói to the north and Syðriflói to the south. The area of the lake is about 38 km², and it lies almost 280 m above sea level. It is shallow, with a mean depth of about 3 m and a maximum depth of about 4.5 m, and is therefore particularly affected by changes in the weather, freezing over early in the winter and becoming quite warm in the summer.

The inflow into Lake Mývatn (about 33 m³ per second) comes mostly from underground springs in an area stretching a few kilometres along its eastern and southern shores. To the north of this area the springwater is warm, but the main inflow is into the southern end of the lake from temperate springs producing cool water. The only significant surface inflow is provided by Grænilækur (about 6 m³ per second), flowing from Lake Grænavatn, which lies just south of Mývatn. The water coming from underneath the lava fields, particularly the hot water, is extremely rich in nutrients, creating ideal conditions to support various forms of aquatic

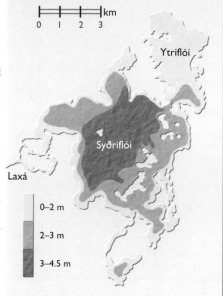

Lake Mývatn is entirely shallow, being mostly 2–3 m deep with a maximum of about 4.5 m. It is interesting to note that in 1880 Þorvaldur Thoroddsen reckoned the depth to be 3½ fathoms (= 6.5 m), and when Ólafsson and Pálsson were writing, around 1750, the maximum depth seems to have been around 9 m. The lake is clearly getting rapidly shallower.

(Sigurjón Rist: Náttúra Íslands)

Underground inflow into Lake Mývatn. Hot groundwater represented by red arrows, cold by blue arrows.

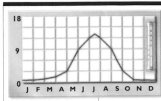

Average water temperature (°C) of the outflow from Lake Mývatn during the years 1972–1988.

The ecology of Lake Mývatn is erratic, being extremely sensitive to changes in the weather and other external factors. In a bad year only a few ducklings make it to adulthood.

life, not to mention the enormous quantity of midges that lend their name to Lake Mývatn ('Midge Lake this, in a nutshell, is the basis for t rich ecology of the lake.

More trout fishing has taken pla here than in other Icelandic lakes, a Mývatn is world famous for its bir life, the most varied of any lake in Iceland.

The lake drains into the river Laxá, which a sh way downstream is joined by the river Kráká – a perennial troublemaker for local farmers because of the sand it brings down from the desert sou of Mývatn. The river Laxá follows the course of the Laxárhraun lava fields down the Laxárda valley, reaching the sea in Skjálfandi Bay. Like the lake itself, the Laxá river supports an extrem rich ecology.

People have long been conscious of the uniqueness of the lake and its ecology. In 1974 t Icelandic Parliament issued a conservation order covering a stretch of land spanning 4,400 km² arou Lake Mývatn and Laxá river. In addition, Lake Mýv and the upper part of Laxá river are protected by terms of the Ramsar Agreement (signed in the Iran city Ramsar, and dealing with the protection of

Lake Mývatn looking northeast.

arshlands that are of international interest, with
rticular respect to their bird life).

Present-day Mývatn is remarkable for great
uctuations in its ecosystem, particularly in recent
cades. During bad periods very few ducklings attain
ulthood, and trout fishing may even fail completely.
ere has been much speculation as to the causes,
d various theories have been proposed. Though
e condition of bird and fish stocks is an obvious
arker, it is generally agreed that there is a complex
teraction of many factors, and research continues
o what is going on.

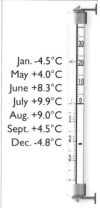

Jan.	-4.5°C
May	+4.0°C
June	+8.3°C
July	+9.9°C
Aug.	+9.0°C
Sept.	+4.5°C
Dec.	-4.8°C

*Average air temperature
in the Mývatn district.*

CLIMATE

eland has a cold temperate climate, with most
habited areas benefiting from the moderating effects
the ocean, but Mývatn, being some distance from
e coast, experiences a greater difference between
erage winter and summer temperatures than other
rts of the country.

Rainfall in Iceland is greatest when the wind is from
e south, and as the Mývatn district is in the rain-
dow of the Vatnajökull glacier, rainfall here is rela-
ely low, being on average just over 400 mm per
ar, a tenth of that which falls on the southern side
of Vatnajökull.

The Mývatn district
usually enjoys high
levels of sunshine, and
can become very warm
during the summer if
the wind is from the
south. On a warm
summer's day it is not
uncommon for the air
temperature to reach
20°C or more, and the
water temperature may
exceed 15°C, making
the lake extraordinarily
fertile considering its
latitude and altitude.

Sometimes, however,
summer can bring

*When Sellandafjall is cloaked in
how a hard winter is on the way.
When Bláfjall is ringed with mist
ood weather will follow. When
he evening sun shines on Bláfjall,
will be dry next day – but when
he evening sun shines on
eykjahlíðarfjall, tomorrow will
ring rain.*

*(From the Folk Tales
of Jón Árnason)*

*A comparison between
average annual rainfall
1961–2000 in the
Mývatn district
(440 mm) and in
Reykjavík (800 mm).*

Höfði in winter.

Höfði in summer.

cold, raw days, when the north wind brin
in sea mist and drizzle to remind one o
the proximity of the Arctic Ocean; even
snow is not unknown at the height of
summer, though it is usually quick to me

In winter the main precipitation is in
the form of snow, which may lie for wee
or even months on end, and there may
long periods of frost, down to as low a
-20° to -30°C. But at least a hard frost
usually accompanied by calm weather.

Even if Lake Mývatn freezes over ear
and is covered in ice all winter, there a
always gaps along the shore where grou
water continues to flow into the lake. I
an average year the ice cover reaches a
thickness of about 70–80 cm, occasiona
reaching a metre or more in a hard win
When there is very little snow on the ice
insulate it from the frost, the edges of
ice expand outwards onto the land, leav
extended ridges in the sand of the lake
creeks and inlets. In a mild winter big ho
in the ice allow the wind to stir the wa
of the lake, and meltwater at just above
freezing point pours into the lake, caus

An ancient book
with runes and
magical spells.

Once the plague of midges around Lake Mývatn was wors
than anyone could remember. Neither man nor beast coul
bear it. A certain man, a bard versed in the magic arts,
composed a poem to exorcize the plague. The moment he
had recited the verse a fierce wind blew in from the north
it lasted for a whole week, bringing such frost and snow
that deep drifts lay on the open land round Mývatn, shee
perished in the snow and two women died from exposur
But there were no more midges round the lake for the re
of that summer.

(From the Folk Tales of Jón Árnaso

...e temperature to drop further than it does when a ...vering of ice keeps it still and insulated from the ...rst frosts. Odd as it may seem, Lake Mývatn therefore ...comes colder during warm winters than otherwise. ...these circumstances slush is formed, which travels ...wn the Laxá river, frequently resulting in flow ...sturbance to the power station situated at the mouth ... Laxárdalur valley, about 30 km below the outflow ...m Lake Mývatn. It is difficult to work out the full ...ects of this on the ecosystem.

▲

Winter scene.
The lake is beginning
to freeze by the shore.

An old etching of Mývatn,
showing vegetation, birds,
and people enjoying a lovely
summer's day. ▼

...EGETATION

...getation in the Mývatn district is luxuriant ... comparison with the rest of Iceland. Of ...e 480 different species of higher plants ...owing throughout Iceland, just under ...50 have been found here.

...The combination of species found is influ-...ced by the bedrock and the climate. Lake ...ývatn is in a volcanically active area, ...ith pumice and drift sand in ...e soil, and the lava fields ...e new and very porous. ...e soil does not retain ...oisture well, so it is ...fficult in many places for ...ants to root, but there are ...merous shallow ponds with

Birch

17

Angelica

luxuriant marsh vegetation well adapted to utilize the light and warmth of the sun. The climate tends to be rather continental compared with other parts of Iceland, and this naturally affects the species combination of the area, as does the presence of geothermal heat. Vegetation undoubtedly suffers greatly from weathering, and a lot of effort is put into cultivating desert areas in order to prevent sandstorms.

To the east and north of the lake are mostly birch forests and thickets, while to the south and west there is marshland and heath. Ponds and marshes are mostly inhabited by sedge grasses. Bottle Sedge (*Carex rostrata*) grows around ponds, and String Sedge (*Carex chordorrhiza*) flourishes

Dandelion

If a man steals Angelica from another's land he shall receive a heavy fine and pay six eyrir by way of compensation.

(from Grágás, The Icelandic National Lawbook, 13th century)

Aaron's Rod. Also known as 'Queen of Mývatn'.

18

the marshy areas between lava outcrops covered with heathers, Dwarf Birch (Betula na), Downy Birch (Betula pubescens) and various pes of willow.

Many of the pseudo-craters and lava outcrops are covered in mosses and lichens, which may be more in evidence than higher ants. On the islets and banks of the lake, rch, Willow and Angelica grow, as well as rious common flowering plants and other pical heath and moorland vegetation. On e high ground west and south of the lake ere are extended moors of heather, Dwarf rch and Willow, and on the islets of the ver Laxá, Willow, Angelica (Angelica archan-ica), Meadow Buttercup (Ranunculus acris) d Wood Cranesbill (Geranium sylvaticum). particular feature of the district, Aaron's Rod, 'Queen of Mývatn' (Erysimum hierachiifolium), very common round Lake Mývatn; it is tall, with ong cluster of yellow flowers, and rarely seen sewhere in Iceland.

The lava fields to the east of the lake are full of eltered areas ideal for observing wild flowers, and a comfortable walking distance from hotels and mping-grounds.

Lichens are very common throughout the area, the ain varieties being Alectoria ochroleuca, Parmelia saxatilis, traria nivalis and Cetraria cucullata (known as 'Mývatn oss').

Iceland Moss (Cetraria islandica), another common hen, has been used all over Iceland, both as a food d (to a lesser extent) for dyeing wool.

Angelica roots and stems were also eaten, mainly ith fish. The right to harvest Angelica was a nsiderable asset, no less valuable than the gathering lichen. Both were covered by ancient law.

> *A man shall not pick berries on another man's land for taking home without permission, but if he does so shall pay double, the same to apply to Iceland Moss should he pick this.*
>
> *(From Landeigubálkur Jónsbókar, a 13th-century law book)*

Iceland Moss

Iceland Moss was mostly used mixed with porridge and skyr (skimmed-milk curd). Picked, cleaned of moss and twigs, and chopped up, it was mainly used to make cereal go further. Often it was boiled whole in milk or a mixture of milk and water, to make a drink called "lichen milk." Sometimes the milk was curdled by mixing rennet with it to make a lichen junket.

Wood Cranesbill
(Geranium sylvaticum)

Adder's Tongue can be found in a few geothermal areas in the Lake Mývatn district.

Lúdentsborgir and Þrengslaborgir. This crater-row was formed about 2,000 years ago when the Younger Laxárhraun lava field was created. It was in this eruption that Lake Mývatn achieved its present-day appearance.

THE ECOLOGY OF THE LAKE

A strand of blue-green algae, the most common plankton in Lake Mývatn most summers.

The spring water flowing into Lake Mývatn originates a considerable distance away, most of it from as far as the Dyngjufjöll range in the central highlands, about 60 km south of Mývatn. Flowing underground for long stretches, it surfaces clean and clear from the bedrock, rich in nutrients which support plankton, plants and bottom-dwelling animals.

Over time a sedimentary layer about six to eight metres thick has formed at the bottom of the lake, made up largely of the shells of diatoms (microscopic algae which secrete silica), and other organic and inorganic substances. By investigating a core sample taken from this sedimentary layer it has been possible to trace the history of the lake's ecology back about 20 centuries, and show that, despite major fluctuations throughout this period, all species currently found in Lake Mývatn have lived there continuously since the lake took on its current form.

Algae bloom in Lake Mývatn. Looking north; Stekkjarnes in the foreground, ▶ clear water in Auðlungaflói Bay in the background.

The sedimentary layer is home to a variety
of bottom-dwelling animals, and the lake bed
is largely covered with vegetation. Among fresh-
water plants growing here and in the numerous
small, shallow pools are Alternate Water Milfoil
(*Myriophyllum alterniflorum*), Sago Pondweed
(*Potamogeton filiformis*) and Water Crowfoot
(*Ranunculus trichophyllus*), particularly where the
water is warmed by geothermal activity.

Diatom ▲
(*Achnanthes lanceolata*
The structure of the silic
shell is clearly visible.

The southern part of the lake contains a large
amount of green algae (Cladophora). These algae can
form balls reaching as much as 10–12 cm in diameter,
covering large areas of the lake bed, and drifting
onto land, where they pile up along the shore.
Sometimes they clog up the locals' trout nets, earning
the sobriquet 'Ball droppings'. In mid-summer the
water of the lake often becomes cloudy with a bloom
of the blue-green algae Anabaena.

The sedimentary layer of the
lake has in recent decades been
utilized as a source for production of diatomite, and a considerable amount of material has been
extracted. We do not have the space
here to discuss the controversy this has caused over
the ecological effects.

▲

Tadpole Shrimp
(*Lepidurus arcticus*), b
far the largest crustacec
in Lake Mývatn, length
around 2 cm.

From Bjarnarflag, This is the main geothermal area
of the Námafjall region. It is exceptionally powerful
and stretches from Bjarnarflag eastwards beyond Hverarönd.

MIDGES

Around 50 types of midge are found by the lake, usually divided into two separate groups, Non-biting or 'Dust Midges' (*Chironomidae*), and Biting (*Simuliidae*) – otherwise known as Black Flies. Bottom-dwelling creatures and plankton are fundamental to the ecology of the lake but the contribution that the midges make is almost the most important.

The midges lay their eggs on the surface of the lake, and as the eggs hatch the larvae sink to the bottom where they settle in the mud. After a variable time on the bottom, they form chrysalides and eventually drift upwards, emerging as fully formed midges from the surface of the water. At all stages of the process they are, along with various bottom-dwelling creatures, an important food source for fish and birds.

By far the more common of the two groups are

The lake gained its name as early as the Age of Settlement because of the untold quantities of midges in the area [...] The lake and the surrounding area are amongst the most remarkable in the whole of Iceland on account of geothermal heat and the extraordinary influence and consequences therefrom.
It is as if Nature has done her utmost to make her presence felt by the locals.

(From the Travel Journal of Eggert Ólafsson and Bjarni Pálsson, the latter half of the 18th century)

A midge emerges from a chrysalis on the surface of the lake.

These are the commonest insects in the north of Iceland: a) Midges. This is the vicious *Water Midge* which greatly afflicts the people and livestock of Mývatn [. . .] bites them, especially cows and horses, so much that blood flows from their eyelids and rumps. Wild with pain, the animals run about, fall or are otherwise injured. On still, sunny summer days the air so fills with these foul visitors that they blot out the sun. If a breeze causes the sky to cloud over, they vanish. It is worst when the sun shines just after rain. Then great clouds of midges hang over the lake shores [. . .] Sometimes the "plague midge" actually kills horses, not by biting them or eating through the skin where it is thinnest, but apparently by entirely filling their orifices. The eyes, ears, noses and mouths are so stuffed with midges that the animal cannot breathe, and suffocates. One thing is sure, when horses run about in fear, they at length exhaust themselves. With their noses stuffed full of midges, the horses have to open their mouths, and then the midges fly in there and down their gullets. The people flee into the caves and chasms which are common in the area, and if they happen to be near a farm they run into the sheep sheds where midges are least likely to go. No solution to this plague has yet been found.

(From the Travel Journal of Eggert Ólafsson and Bjarni Pálsson, latter half of the 18th century)

the 'Dust Midges', so called because as breeding time approaches the male midges create dark columns, like clouds of dust in the air, with the aim of attracting females. The 'Dust Midges' hatch mainly in the lake itself. They bite neither human nor animal, yet can be a nuisance by their sheer numbers.

Black Flies hatch their eggs in moving water, mostly in Laxá river and by the out-flow from Mývatn. Often called 'Plague Midges', they suck both human and animal blood and can be extremely troublesome. It is only the females that attack, and they are particularly hungry as hatching time approaches.

The midge population varies from year to year. Normally midges hatch twice during the summer, but some years they are fewer in number. It is very obvious when they are flying, and sometimes the swarm is so dense that it is better for everybody (animals included) to stay indoors. Birds and fish, however, have a feast.

Fly-swatter – a useful weapon in Mývatn.

This monster is considered to be so repugnant that it is impossible to imagine that the midge, which causes such devastation, can have been created by God; rather it must have come to life in the Devil's beard, and consequently midges are known as "Lice from the Devil's beard".

(Jón Árnason's Folk Tales)

Plants, too, exploit the midges, which on death are absorbed into the ground as fertilizer. It is worth reminding oneself on those still, sunny days when the midges are making a nuisance of themselves, that the whole environment would be very different without them.

Midge columns. ▲
The males form column swarms during mating; this behaviour serves to attract females.

Fish

Three types of fish are found in the waters of Mývatn and Laxá: the Arctic Charr (*Salvelinus alpinus*), Brown Trout (*Salmo trutta*), and the Three-spined Stickleback (*Gasterosteus aculeatus*).

Both the Charr and the Brown Trout have always been important exploited species, particularly the Charr, which is far the more numerous in Mývatn, and spawns mainly in the southern part of the lake. It feeds mainly on midge pupae and larvae and other small creatures. Three sub-species of Charr have been identified in the lake, representing adaptations to variations in circumstances and feeding opportunities.

The Three-spined Stickle back is the most comm fish in Mývatn. They ar usually around 4—5 cm length but examples up 10 cm long have been fou in Mývatn.

Though less important nowadays, charr and trout fishing has always played a significant part in the local economy throughout the year; as much as a third of the annual

Brown Trout

26

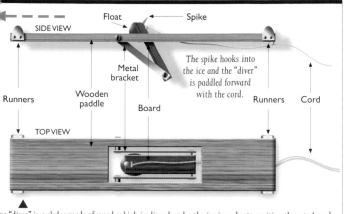

SIDE VIEW

Float — Spike

The spike hooks into the ice and the "diver" is paddled forward with the cord.

Metal bracket

Runners — Wooden paddle — Board — Runners — Cord

TOP VIEW

The "diver" is a sledge made of wood, which is slipped under the ice in order to position the net. A cord is attached to the back of the sledge, and repeated tugs on the cord cause the paddle to propel the diver forwards. When the diver has travelled far enough for the length of net, the fisherman measures out its position, hacks or drills a hole in the ice, and pulls the diver through. Then the net is attached to the cord and pulled back under the ice. The local people adopted this contrivance during the 1930s; a Mývatn man who had emigrated to Canada heard of it from Native Canadians and sent drawings of it back to his friends.

net under the ice.

total is caught during the winter months through holes in the ice, using both lines and nets.

Records going back to around 1900 show that the size of the catch has always been extremely variable from year to year, with a mean annual catch during the 20th century of about 35,000 rising to a maximum of 100,000. Caught fish are generally around a pound in weight, though larger ones are very common. Smoked charr or trout has been a long-time favourite

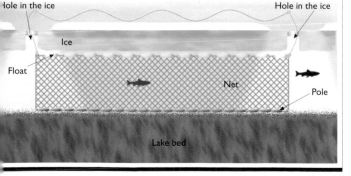

Hole in the ice — Hole in the ice

Ice

Float — Net — Pole

Lake bed

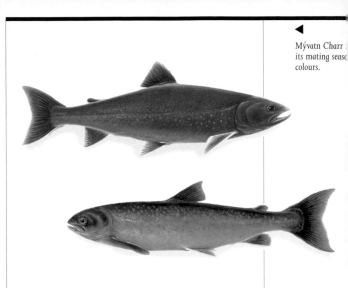

Mývatn Charr
its mating seaso
colours.

on local dinner tables, and will no doubt continue
to be so. There used to be a considerable trade in
wind-dried fish, though this is no longer so; and
around 1930 there was some export of
salted fillets of trout, mainly to France.

Though fishing has diminished in

Rod fishing at Mývatn. The fisherman is pleased with
his catch. The maggot jar can be seen by his left foot.
This picture was taken in 1965.

Bait was got by killing a dog, letting
it rot until it was crawling with
maggots, and then freezing it.
When winter came the carcass was
cut up and the maggots picked
out and put into a tin, which the
fisherman kept close to his body
so the maggots would thaw out
and come alive. It is said that some
didn't flinch from thawing the
maggots in their mouths, as they
had to wriggle on the hook for
the trout to take the bait.

*(Jónas Jónasson from Hrafnagil:
Icelandic Folk Customs)*

28

▲

Icelandic rivers are a magnet for celebrities. This picture of Bing Crosby was taken in 1969 in Laxá in Aðaldalur.

▼ Staðarhraun Shrimp — an artificial fly, good for catching Brown Trout.

importance to the local economy, the catch remains a useful means of monitoring the state of the lake's ecology.

Brown Trout, less numerous than Charr in the lake itself, dominate the upper part of Laxá river. They spawn in moving water and live almost entirely off Black-fly larvae, which hatch in the same environment as the fish. Other small fish and even ducklings also feature on the Trout's menu. The upper part of Laxá, which stretches from the outflow from Mývatn down towards the Brúar power station, about 30 km in all, is the best known and most abundant trout fishing region in the country. The river's reputation has travelled far beyond Iceland, and it is considered by anglers to be one of the best trout rivers in the world. Fish weighing between three and five pounds are regularly caught, with 10–15 pound fish being not uncommon. In this area only fly-fishing is permitted; it is considered to be nobler than other methods, demanding of the fisherman a great deal of skill and dexterity.

Finally, the Three-spined Stickleback is the smallest and most common species found in Mývatn. During recent years attention has focused on its importance in the food chain; Red-breasted Mergansers feed almost entirely on Stickleback, and its roe is an important food for both Charr and Trout. It is also a competitor with Charr and Trout for other food sources.

Mývatn is the most prominent lake in the North and, as far as trout fishing is concerned, the most important lake in the whole of Iceland [...] The locals live off trout fishing and have done so as long as the area has been inhabited. They never go sea-fishing, nor do they purchase fish. On every farm there is a boat and dozens of nets, 10–30 fathoms in length. They are woven from a fine jute thread, which the locals themselves spin.

(From the Travel Journal of Eggert Ólafsson and Bjarni Pálsson, latter half of the 18th century)

A peat-smoked ▲ trout from Mývatn.

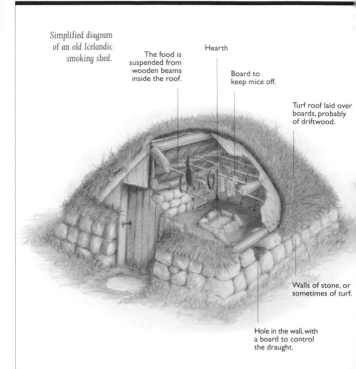

Simplified diagram of an old Icelandic smoking shed.

The food is suspended from wooden beams inside the roof.

Hearth

Board to keep mice off.

Turf roof laid over boards, probably of driftwood.

Walls of stone, or sometimes of turf.

Hole in the wall, with a board to control the draught.

Inside the smoking shed at Skútustaðir.

BARROW'S GOLDENEYE (Bucephala islandica)
remarkable in that it originates from North
America and does not nest elsewhere in Europe
other than in Iceland, where it is resident almost
exclusively in the Mývatn and Laxá area.

Barrow's Goldeneye often nest in crevices
in the stone walls of houses and barns, and
this has inspired the bird's Icelandic name,
'House Duck'. The local people at
Mývatn have exploited this behaviour
by putting up nesting-boxes in barns
and outhouses. Of all species found in
the area, this is the most dependent on the
local conditions, not merely because of its nesting

habits, but also its choice of food, relying on midge larvae and other bottom-dwelling creatures.
There is a marked difference in size between the genders. Drakes are large and stocky; they
need physical strength, for during courting they are extremely territorial and fierce defenders
of their domains. Females are smaller, which is a definite advantage when it comes to nesting
in narrow crevices. The courting season is lengthy and rather lively, the drakes becoming very
frisky as spring sets in. Most Barrow's Goldeneye remain in the Mývatn area all year round.

The **HARLEQUIN DUCK** (Histrionicus histrionicus) is also American in origin and
nests throughout Iceland, occupying the banks of fast-flowing rivers during nesting time and
well into the summer. Here it particularly favours the upper part of river Laxá, just below
the outflow from Lake Mývatn. During the nesting season the Harlequin Duck lives off the
larvae of the Black Fly, which it is adept at finding
amongst the rocks of the rapids.
The chicks are precocious, and
are fearless divers, their survival
depending entirely on the harvest
offered by the river. The drakes'
breeding plumage is extremely
colourful, but serves admirably
as camouflage, whether in the
tumult of the rapids or in the angry
surf of a rocky shore. Drakes return to
the sea at the end of June, and by the
beginning of September most of the rest
of the Harlequin Duck population has
joined them to spend the winter there.

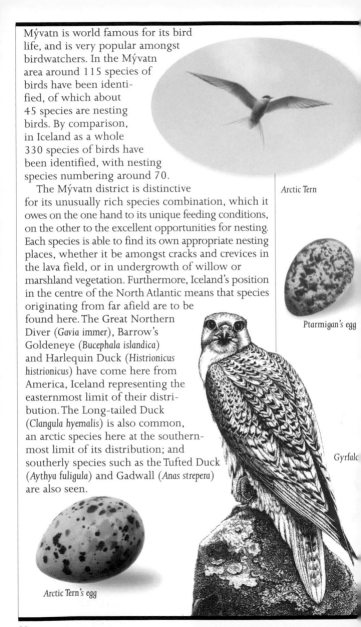

Mývatn is world famous for its bird life, and is very popular amongst birdwatchers. In the Mývatn area around 115 species of birds have been identified, of which about 45 species are nesting birds. By comparison, in Iceland as a whole 330 species of birds have been identified, with nesting species numbering around 70.

Arctic Tern

The Mývatn district is distinctive for its unusually rich species combination, which it owes on the one hand to its unique feeding conditions, on the other to the excellent opportunities for nesting. Each species is able to find its own appropriate nesting places, whether it be amongst cracks and crevices in the lava field, or in undergrowth of willow or marshland vegetation. Furthermore, Iceland's position in the centre of the North Atlantic means that species originating from far afield are to be found here. The Great Northern Diver (*Gavia immer*), Barrow's Goldeneye (*Bucephala islandica*) and Harlequin Duck (*Histrionicus histrionicus*) have come here from America, Iceland representing the easternmost limit of their distribution. The Long-tailed Duck (*Clangula hyemalis*) is also common, an arctic species here at the southernmost limit of its distribution; and southerly species such as the Tufted Duck (*Aythya fuligula*) and Gadwall (*Anas strepera*) are also seen.

Ptarmigan's egg

Gyrfalc

Arctic Tern's egg

32

There are various other species of nesting birds we have not yet mentioned. The Arctic Tern (*Sterna paradisaea*) is common round Mývatn, also the Black-headed Gull (*Larus ridibundus*), Whooper Swan (*Cygnus cygnus*), Red-necked Phalarope (*Phalaropus lobatus*) and several other varieties of wader. Not so prominent or widespread are species such as the Red-throated Diver (*Gavia stellata*), Slavonian Grebe (*Podiceps auritus*), Gyrfalcon (*Falco rusticolus*), Merlin (*Falco columbarius*) and Ptarmigan (*Lagopus mutus*).

igeon

Not surprisingly, water and marshland birds are the most common species around Mývatn, with ducks without doubt pre-eminent. Apart from the Eider (*Somateria mollissima*), every variety of duck

pe

that nests in Iceland nests round Mývatn and the upper part of river Laxá. Around 16 duck varieties nest continuously in the area, and it would be hard to find a lake anywhere with as dense or varied a nesting duck population. The total number of adult ducks around Mývatn in the summer, though variable from year to year, must be well over 10,000 nesting pairs.

To maintain steady population levels, Nature allows for wastage by ensuring that ducks lay large clutches of eggs. Numbers vary according to different species, but some females may lay up to 10–12 eggs at a time. The crucial determinant of the viability of the Mývatn duck population is generally agreed to be the availability of food. In some seasons when food is scarce (e.g. if the supply of midges dwindles), the size of clutches and the number of ducklings reared will fall off, but as a rule of thumb one can say that in a good year each female will raise on average four to five ducklings. Previously, eggs were laid on densely populated islets

eylag goslings
the nest are a rare sight,
they leave the nest soon
er hatching.

where they were safe from foxes, but the ducks' nesting habits changed somewhat after mink invaded the Mývatn district around 1950. Although the arrival of the mink does not seem to have noticeably reduced the duck population, it has caused their nesting area to be somewhat more spread out than before, and they seem to prefer nesting near Black-headed Gulls and Arctic Terns, in order to enjoy their protection.

A dabbling duck above, fish-eating duck below. Notice their very different bea

Ducks feed on a variety of foods, both animal and vegetable, the shape of their beaks being adapted to their particular feeding preferences. The duck species at Mývatn can be divided into three main groups according to how they make use of the various conditions offered by the lake.

Dabbling ducks are mainly vegetarians, and search for food on the surfaces of lakes and along riverbanks. They rarely dive, but upend and stretch down to search for bottom-dwelling creatures and vegetation in shallow waters. At Mývatn they also feed on midges.

Diving ducks stick mainly to food-rich shallow waters, and are very common in the Lake Mývatn area. Though they mostly take food from the lake bottom, they may also feed from the surface of the lake, especially after the midges start to surface in early summer. Their beaks are well adapted to sifting the various small creatures from the sediment on the lake bed, a task made easy by the shallowness of these waters. This shallowness plays a very important part in supporting the rich bird life in the area. Diving ducks restrict themselves to a depth of about three metres when feeding, and it has to be said that their opportunities have been somewhat curtailed in recent decades by the diatomite extraction industry.

Short-eared C — often seen i the Mývatn ar

The third group is the fish-eating ducks, whose choice of food is indicated by their name. They are extremely well suited for fishing, the beak being narrow and serrated, ending in a kind of hook at the tip.

The duck nesting-grounds have always been exploited by the locals, with duck eggs forming an important part of their diet. Eggs are usually eaten fresh, but at one time they were also buried in ash and stored for winter. They keep for months in ash, with the inside turning over time into a cheese-like jelly. The uninitiated may find the smell unpleasant, and indeed it has become rare for anyone to eat eggs preserved in this way.

Short-eared Owl on the lookout for prey — mice or fledglings.

During the first half of the 20th century, Mývatn farmers took up to 30–40,000 eggs each year. Early records show that the locals have always taken care to maintain a sustainable exploitation of the nesting grounds by not taking too many eggs. In earlier times four or five were usually left in each nest, though nowadays it is usual to remove only about two eggs, which clearly presents no danger to the ducks' breeding viability.

Around the beginning of the 20th century, some farmers began keeping formal records of the numbers of eggs collected, and also tried to classify the eggs they took by species. These records, together with other observations and population counts, have proved invaluable to scientists in their analysis of duck numbers and breeding patterns in Mývatn. This is true also of many other basic observations in relation to the natural history of the Lake Mývatn area, and it is worth noting that the data compiled by these local people, brought up to do traditional farmwork, and without the benefit of specialized education in biological sciences, have proved crucial to the scientific study of the area.

BIRDWATCHING IN THE LAKE MÝVATN AREA

Good places for birdwatching include Höfði, Kálfastrandarvogar and Neslandavík, as well as the shore near Skútustaðir and the banks of the Laxá river.

The northern shore of Lake Mývatn has many inlets and pools teeming with birds; of these, only the main species will be covered in this book. Visitors should be aware that access to some of these areas is, at least partially, restricted to roads and defined paths during the nesting season – roughly speaking the two months between May 15 and July 20.

Birdwatchers can find something of interest throughout the year. Even when the lake is frozen over in winter there will be flocks of birds in gaps and holes in the ice, with swans, Barrow's Goldeneye and Goosander prominent.

Spring, however, is without doubt by far the best season for birdwatching. The first migrating birds, such as the Black-headed Gull, Tufted Duck and

Map showing the main birdwatching areas near Mývatn

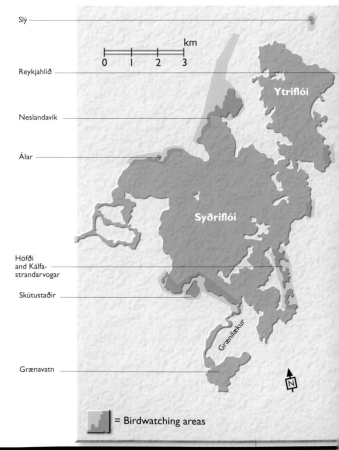

*Red-throated Diver
sitting on its nest.*

Slavonian Grebe, start arriving in April, and by the
end of May all the migrants have arrived. Vegetation
is still sparse, so it is easy to see birds and observe
their behaviour, which is very lively at this time
of year. The courting season is in full swing, and the
males, sporting their colourful breeding plumage,
fight a relentless territorial battle. Dust Midges come
to life at the beginning of June and though their
columnar swarms can be a nuisance, they are
an essential natural feature of the area.

The birds become less boisterous as summer
progresses. Towards the latter half of June, the drakes
gather in flocks to moult; within a short period the
brilliant colours of their breeding plumage have
vanished. Females remain by their nests, while the
drakes, their part in the breeding process accomplished,
disappear off the scene; Harlequins and Common
Scoters making for the sea, dabbling-duck species
lying low amongst the sedges around the lake. Towards
the middle of July the females drive the ducklings
out of their nests and are soon to be seen in their
thousands on the lake with their young. The ducklings
grow quickly, and by August there is not much
difference between their plumage and that of the
fully grown females. Now it may be difficult to
distinguish between species. In late summer swans
gather in moulting flocks on the lake, and Red-necked
Phalaropes are widely to be seen.

In September snow falls in the mountains. The
migrating birds begin to leave the area and all are
gone by the end of October. Snow Bunting, Raven,
Ptarmigan and Gyrfalcon are among those that remain.

PRINCIPAL SPECIES OF BIRDS IN THE MÝVATN REGIO

Great Northern Diver (*Gavia immer*)

Red-throated Diver (*Gavia stellata*)

Slavonian Grebe (*Podiceps auritus*)

Whooper Swan (*Cygnus cygnus*)

Greylag Goose (*Anser anser*)

Pink-footed Goose
(*Anser brachyrhynchus*)

Mallard (*Anas platyrhynchos*)

Wigeon (*Anas penelope*)

~ American Wigeon (*Anas americana*)

Teal (*Anas crecca*)

Gadwall (*Anas strepera*)

Pintail (*Anas acuta*)

~ Shoveler (*Anas clypeata*)

Scaup (*Aythya marila*)

Tufted Duck (*Aythya fuligula*)

~ Pochard (*Aythya ferina*)

Barrow's Goldeneye
(*Bucephala islandica*)

~ Goldeneye (*Bucephala clangula*)

Harlequin Duck
(*Histrionicus histrionicus*)

Common Scoter (*Melanitta nigra*)

Long-tailed Duck (*Clangula hyemalis*)

Goosander (*Mergus merganser*)

Red-breasted Merganser
(*Mergus serrator*)

~ Ruddy Duck (*Oxyura jamaicensis*)

Gyrfalcon (*Falco rusticolus*)

Merlin (*Falco columbarius*)

Ptarmigan (*Lagopus mutus*)

Ringed Plover (*Charadrius hiaticula*)

Golden Plover (*Pluvialis apricaria*)

Dunlin (*Calidris alpina*)

Black-tailed Godwit (*Limosa limosa*)

Whimbrel (*Numenius phaeopus*)

Snipe (*Gallinago gallinago*)

Redshank (*Tringa totanus*)

Purple Sandpiper (*Calidris maritima*)

Red-necked Phalarope
(*Phalaropus lobatus*)

Here are listed the regular nesting birds
the Mývatn region, together with a few
of the more common visitors. There is r
space in this publication to cover all spec
that have ever been sighted.

The species are arranged by family accord
to the classification most usually adopte
readers should refer to more specialized
handbooks for detailed identifications.

Arctic Skua
(*Stercorarius parasiticus*)

Great Black-backed Gull
(*Larus marinus*)

Black-headed Gull (*Larus ridibundus*)

Arctic Tern (*Sterna paradisaea*)

~ Snowy Owl (*Nyctea scandiaca*)

Short-eared Owl (*Asio flammeus*)

Raven (*Corvus corax*)

Redwing (*Turdus iliacus*)

Wheatear (*Oenanthe oenanthe*)

White Wagtail (*Motacilla alba*)

Meadow Pipit (*Antus pratensis*)

Wren (*Troglodytes troglodytes*)

Redpoll (*Carduelis flammea*)

Snow Bunting (*Plectrophenax nivalis*)

~ Brambling (*Fringilla montefringilla*)

~ Rare

The Great Northern Diver. Several pairs nest in the Mývatn area.

Slavonian Grebe and chick.

Long-tailed drake

WILD MAMMALS

Because Iceland has always been geographically isolated, there are very few native species of wild mammals. In the Mývatn area there are only three: Arctic Fox (*Alopex lagopus*), Field Mouse (*Apodemus sylvaticus*) and Mink (*Mustela vison*). During the 19th century there were also reindeer, but they have since vanished.

Arctic Fox

The Arctic Fox lives in the Arctic area, the southern boundary of its distribution area largely following the Arctic Circle. These are the only wild mammals to have reached Iceland without human assistance. During the glacial period their habitat extended as far as Southern Europe, but they then followed the Ice Age glacier as it retreated northwards. This is how the fox came to be in Iceland, and a few will have been left behind as the glacial bridge broke between Iceland and Greenland. It is also possible that foxes may have been brought here on drift ice from Greenland.

In this publicatio… about chick… farming, publ… in 1915, there is son… useful advice on how… defend hen houses aga… the fox. Another pest … soon to create headach… the chicken farmer an… hens: this was the mi… first imported in 193…

In Iceland foxes are great opportunists as far as choosing food is concerned. They will eat carrion and salt-water fish as well as birds, eggs and berries. They have long been considered to be serious pests, as they are known to attack the weaker lambs and raid bird colonies. In the most ancient laws there are clauses encouraging the killing of foxes, and since time immemorial rewards have been offered for their destruction. A few decades ago the fox population in Iceland had fallen to crisis point, the numbers caught seeming to

d Mouse

ık

indicate a significant decline. They now seem to be on the increase again, particularly near densely populated areas where garbage is found, such as from the fishing industry. At one time foxes were common in the Mývatn area, but they are now seldom to be seen.

Field mice are widespread throughout most of Eurasia, and it is thought that they arrived in Iceland with the first human settlers about 1,100 years ago. They are more common in fertile areas, but are also found in lava fields, such as those around Mývatn. They often live in close quarters with people, and used to cause great destruction, especially in years when their numbers were high; but improved sanitation and better housing has largely removed the problem. Their predators in Iceland are foxes, minks, the Short-eared Owl, and possibly other birds.

Minks originate in North America and were originally imported to Iceland in 1931 with a view to cultivation for their much sought-after fur. Poor caging and general carelessness soon allowed a few creatures to escape, resulting in the establishment of a wild mink population in Iceland, and a rapid realization of the havoc wrought by mink on the ecology of the country. They spread incredibly quickly, breeding rapidly and enjoying particularly advantageous conditions in the hunt for food. Only 20 years after the first minks came to Iceland mink cultivation was banned by law. It was too late. In 35 years the mink population spread all over the country, bringing irremediable loss to the ecology, bird life especially. Mink cultivation was permitted again in 1969. Attempts continue to eradicate the wild population wherever possible, with limited success, though experience has shown that by combining knowledge of their habits with good organization and vigilance, it is possible to curtail their further spread.

Midnight

Little is known about the beginnings of settlement in the area, nor is there much documentary evidence from the Middle Ages. On the other hand, there have been significant archaeological finds from the early years of settlement in Iceland, such as some pagan graves and the remains of a Viking long-house at Hofsstaðir by Laxá.

*ving of
ja-age farm.*

The most noteworthy grave was found near Baldursheimur farm in the spring of 1860. Here, a man had been laid to rest along with his horse, weapons and other artefacts, including the remains of a spear, sword, axe, knife and shield, and the components of an early board game ('*hnefatafl*'). Here was a nobleman worthy of welcome in the halls of Valhalla.

The ruins at Hofsstaðir were long thought to be an example of the so-called Viking 'temple-farm', but it is now believed this unusually large Saga-age long-house was not a temple but rather a banqueting hall where men gathered to celebrate after sacrificial ceremonies. The structure is 45 m long and over 8 m in width at its widest, and will have been one of the most impressive buildings of its time in the country. An international team of archaeologists recently carried out investigations into the Hofsstaðir site, and it is hoped that these researches will throw light on early living conditions in the Mývatn district.

*·ds were the most
·rate and valuable of
·eapons carried in the
·ng age. The blade was
·ly double-edged, the
·d straight and the
·le short.*

From earliest days the locals, as well as being sheep farmers, exploited the bounty of the lake, with its trout fishing and egg collecting, and enjoyed an unusually secure existence.

43

The climate, too, allowed them to leave their sheep out on the hills to graze long into the autumn. Nowadays the inhabited area has shrunk, and the remoter farms, which were still being worked well into the 20th century, have been abandoned. Some farms have always had two or more households sharing the estate; today there are probably about 50 farms on just over 20 estates.

For centuries sulphur, an important raw material in the making of gunpowder, was extracted from nearby volcanic areas, albeit intermittently and in varying amounts; this continued during the Middle Ages and through to the latter half of the 19th century, and again briefly around 1940.

In modern times there has been a huge increase in the non-farming population of the Mývatn district, and the appearance of the district has changed completely, with built-up areas springing up around the diatomite extraction plant and the Krafla geothermal power station. The expanding tourist industry, too, has become an increasingly valuable source of local income, for farmers as well as others. The inhabitants of the Mývatn district now number around 500 in all.

The Mývatn district, formerly a somewhat remote area, has during the 20th century been brought into the public spotlight. Iceland's main highway crosses the county, and the summer influx of tourists probably makes up the greater part of all journeys made into the area. The profits from the tourist industry are

. . . large gangs of men have hacked away and excavated those mountains in the north of the country where there are great quantities of this resource. Therefore, it being first sought thence for the benefit of the Danish realm, two or three cargo ships were despatched to Iceland every year to transport many tonnes of sulphur from the northern coast.

(Bishop Oddur Einarsson's Íslandslýsing, end of the 16th century)

▲ Farmers going to market around the beginning of the 20th century.

◄ The sledge was extrem useful for transportin or goods in winter. I pulled by horses.

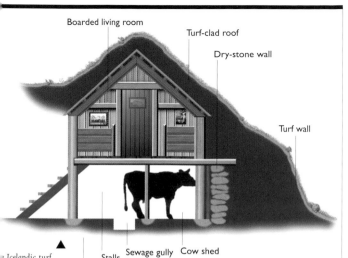

Boarded living room | Turf-clad roof | Dry-stone wall | Turf wall

Stalls | Sewage gully | Cow shed

Icelandic turf
nhouses were in fact
ber houses with a
ding of turf. The heat
n the cows rose and
vided the inhabitants
h warmth in cold
ters. Poorer farmers
n kept sheep and even
s in the living room.

walls of Icelandic ▶
houses were built with
or stone. Stone formed
undation for turf walls,
turf was used in
rmediate layers in stone
s. Earth was used as a
r and as a sealant and
lator. Turf was cut into
ous shapes to form the
ding blocks required.

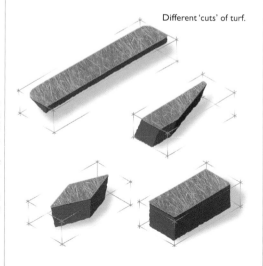

Different 'cuts' of turf.

Sheep pens at Baldursheimur.

simply a new form of exploitation of Mývatn's natural resources, and even the most traditionalist farmers are aware of this. The preservation of those natural resources is their best guarantee of maintaining the viability of the local economy.

As elsewhere in Iceland, the annual round-up of sheep is a busy time. The Mývatn district is surrounded by wilderness, and the sheep are widely dispersed around the summer pastures that are scattered amongst lava fields and rocky outcrops. The round-up lasts about five days during the first half of September, with a further search for stragglers later in the autumn, and requires considerable manpower; a round-up manager is appointed to supervise the operation, and farmers contribute to the cost according to the size of their flocks.

During their search, the men stay overnight in huts or shelters up in the highlands. In the old days they would have travelled on foot or horseback, but

A drover

In the sheep pens, then . . .

. . . a now.

46

Christmas party at Haganes in 1906.

nowadays they use jeeps and motor sledges, along with modern telecommunication devices, to speed the search.

Finally the sheep are driven in their thousands into a corral and sorted into individual pens for recovery by their owners. People come from far and wide to meet old friends and enjoy a song and dance and a few drinks. At the end of it all, the sheep are driven back to the farms and kept in home pastures until the time comes for the slaughter.

Although the Mývatn district used to be remote, the locals have always been a sociable lot and open to outside cultural influence. Patterns of life have been much affected by the ice on the lake, which provides a winter short cut between farms. One could say that the lake's covering of ice formed the foundation of this isolated area's social life, and helped keep it active.

As one would expect, the people of Mývatn have had to be self-sufficient for their recreations and entertainment. The district was for a long time a centre for the Icelandic national sport of wrestling ('glíma'), and the 19th century saw asm for sports such as skating and swimming.

A budding wrestling champion enjoying the sun in the middle of a hayfield.

Then there were the harvest festivals, celebrated communally when haymaking and other autumn tasks were done.

During the 19th century moves were made to develop commercial and educational co-operation in the area. A Reading Society was established, as well as agricultural and trading associations. In 1858 in the parish Skútustaðir a 'Farm Workers' Savings Bank' was set up, undoubtedly the first bank in Iceland. Farmers' housing was improved, and progress was made in various agricultural techniques, such as sheep breeding.

All this led to a truly unique appetite for culture in the area, amongst whose more notable manifestations were book-buying syndicate and series of public meetings that quickly acquired considerable influence. Hand-written local periodicals were published and circulated, with as many as three different titles appearing at one time. To begin with, they carried mainly humorous and general interest material, but as time passed, they began to sound a more serious note; the position of women in society seems to have particularly captured peoples' interest, and class distinction, the power of officialdom and ill-treatment of animals were also subjects of criticism.

For a time, free schooling was provided – this was the first youth education initiative in Iceland. The Reading Society was in favour of buying Danish books for its lending library rather than Icelandic. One reason offered was that the native publishing industry would suffer if people borrowed Icelandic books instead of buying them; but foreign books were also seen as more original, more practical, and as providing more useful fare for people to take with them on the road to progress. The subject matter of new books was a popular topic for discussion at local public meetings.

In closing, it should be mentioned that the farmers of Mývatn have been active in the field of poetry, and contributed their fair share to the enrichment of Icelandic literature.

Norðri, útWtas 3. blað sem geymst var til / Mývatnssveit 1884-1885

Norðri, a magazine published in the Mývatn district in 1884–1885. Norðri was one of the handwritten local periodicals, which were passed around. A few copies are preserved in the museum in Húsavík.

Being able to "read" the clouds was, and still is, very important to the farmer: "Will it rain on my mown grass tomorrow?"
These pictures are of cloud formations over Mývatn, all taken on the same day.

The farmhouse at Skútustaðir in 1912.

A farmer and a haycart.

Farmers from
Reykjahlíð during
haymaking in 1926.

The farm at Reykjahlíð.
Notice the mill. Hotel
Reynihlíð is now situated
where these houses once
stood.

• **Arnarbæli:** An individual pseudo-crater on the south coast of Lake Mývatn. At one time Sea Eagles (*Haliæetus albicilla*) were frequently seen in the Mývatn district and almost certainly nested there. The place-names Arnarbæli ('Eagle's Lair') and Arnarvatn ('Eagle Lake') reflect this.

• **Arnarvatn:** A shallow lake a short distance south west of Lake Mývatn, formed when the Younger Laxárhraun lava field blocked the Mývatn basin. The river Helluvaðsá runs from the lake into Laxá river.

• **Arnarvatn:** A farm, home of the poet Sigurður Jónsson (1878-1949) – the "national poet" of Mývatn.

• **Baldursheimur:** A farm, best known for the pagan grave discovered there in 1860. The name of the farm is probably derived from the name of the heathen god Baldur, and is the only place-name in Iceland connected with this god. In the first half of the 20th century Þórólfur Sigurðsson lived here (1886-1940). He was very concerned with social affairs and the trade union movement, and founded the magazine "Réttur" ('Justice'), the first Icelandic periodical on social affairs. He was against "favouritism and privileges" and strove for "not only legal but natural justice".

• **Belgjarfjall:** An individual tuff mountain (529 m) northwest of Lake Mývatn *(see also Vindbelgjarfjall)*.

• **Bjarnarflag:** Geothermal area about four kilometres east of Lake Mývatn. Highway 1 runs through the area. **B.** suffered some volcanic activity during the Mývatn Eruption 1724–1729. Iceland's first steam power station was built here to provide electricity for a factory that utilizes the silicon from the bed of Lake Mývatn for the production of diatomite *(see also Kísiliðjan)*. The steam is also used to dry the diatomite, and in the production of hollow concrete blocks and bricks. During the Krafla Eruptions (1975–1984) this was the scene of a freak event when a jet of lava gushed out of a borehole.

• **Bláfjall:** A table mountain (1,222 m) south of Lake Mývatn, formed during the most recent glacial period in a sub-glacial eruption on the northern part of the volcanic area which straddles the country. The mountain can be seen far and wide, and there are fine views from the summit.

• **Bláhvammur:** Tall and dramatic tuff cliffs, and a rocky ravine with stretches of vegetation and birch, situated below Bláfjall, just under ten kilometres south of Lake Mývatn. Bláhvammur is within walking distance of the farm Garður and Grænavatn (ca. 2½ hours). The route lies over a relatively even and dry lava field and sands. This walk could be linked with one to Seljahjallagil, which is just north of Bláhvammur. Thirsty walkers should note that there is no drinking water to be found on this route.

• **Búrfell:** A table mountain (953 m) east of Lake Mývatn. The mountain was formed during a sub-glacial eruption on the northern part of the volcanic area which straddles the country, and is easily visible from Mývatn.

• **Búrfellshraun:** A lava field named after Búrfell (*see above*), although it does not originate there, being considerably younger, having flowed after the end of the last Ice Age. Highway 1 runs through the north end of the lava field from Námaskarð eastwards over the Mývatn wilderness.

• **Dalfjall:** A mountain range (just over 500 m) consisting mostly of pillow lava formed during a sub-glacial fissure eruption. Further eruptions have taken place here since the end of the Ice Age. Dalfjall, along with Námafjall, forms a 15 km long ridge. There is a 2–2½ hour walk from Námaskarð north towards Leirhnjúkur. This walk takes in a variety of rock formations, and there is a fine view from the mountain towards the lake in the west and the desert in the east, all the way to Mount Herðubreið.

• **Dimmuborgir:** Unique rock formations in the Younger Laxárhraun, these are among the best known natural phenomena in the Mývatn district. There is a wide variety of the most amazing shapes, lava pillars and keyhole rocks, of which the so-called "Church" has to be the most famous. On its journey westwards the lava has collected in hollows, filling them to

Dimmuborgir

51

create ponds of molten lava; as the topmost layer cooled down, its surface formed a thin shell, which subsequently collapsed as the lava flowed away from underneath it, emptying the lava ponds. Since the hollows will have originally contained water (probably spring water), steam explosions will also have helped to create the myriad lava chimneys and cones of **D.** There are posted footpaths within **D.**, and there is also a posted route between **D.** and Hverfjall (about 1 hour up to the edge of the crater).

• **Eldá:** The lava stream which flowed towards the end of the Mývatn eruption in the summer of 1729 from Leirhnjúkur all the way to Lake Mývatn. The lava reached the north end of the lake and destroyed three farms. The church at Reykjahlíð was completely surrounded but survived unscathed as it stood on a small hillock. A straightforward and easy walk (3–4 hours) skirts **E.** between Leirhnjúkur and Reykjahlíð.

• **Eldhraun:** A lava field at the north end of Lake Mývatn, which flowed during the final stages of the Mývatn eruption in the summer of 1729.

• **Framengjar:** Marshland with numerous small lakes and ponds south of Lake Mývatn. At one time the meadows of the flood plain were an important source of hay for local farmers. During haymaking they set up camp here. The hay was stacked in hay-shelters, to be fetched by sledge during winter.

• **Fremri-Námar:** Geothermal area in Ketildyngja, about 25 km southeast of Mývatn. At one time an important source of sulphur for export. There were other sulphur mines in the area, but here it was considered purer than elsewhere and easier to extract. Once mined, though, it had to be transported to the nearest harbour, four days' journey away.

• **Gautlönd:** A farm; birthplace of Jón Sigurðsson (1828-1889), the leading figure in the nationalist movement during the struggle for independence from Denmark.

• **Geirastaðir:** A farm mentioned in the Book of Settlements (which chronicled the original 9th-century settlers of Iceland) as follows: "A Norseman there was, named Geiri, who first dwelt south of Mývatn, at Geirastaðir. . ."

- **Geiteyjarströnd:** A farm; an important centre in the days when dragnet fishing (now banned) was prevalent in Mývatn.
- **Gjástykki:** A stretch of land, which is a part of the fissure belt between Mývatn and Öxarfjörður. There are many parallel fissures here, stretching from south to north. The land has cracked and the ground level fluctuated in periods of volcanic activity. During the Krafla Eruptions of 1975–1984 most of the lava came up through rifts in **G**. The new lava here has in many places formed a thin skin with hollows beneath; this lava crust is liable to break when trodden on, and so the area is, in places, not entirely safe to walk on. Those intending to explore the area should be aware of this. Here, as in many other places round Mývatn, there is no drinking water to be found.
- **Grjótagjá:** Fault fissure with hot water about two km east of Mývatn. There is a brisk flow of water through **G.**, and the river used to be a popular bathing area. After the earth tremors started during the Krafla Eruptions in the winter of 1975, the fissure became unsuitable for bathing, because the temperature of the water rose considerably (it reached 60°C at its hottest but has now cooled somewhat) and there was great danger of rock-falls. Between Reykjahlíð and **G.** there is a posted hike (about 45 min.) and from **G.** there is a hike up to Hverfjall (about 1 hour up to the edge of the crater) and from there towards Dimmuborgir (the whole route takes about 3 hours).

- **Grjótavogur:** Here, at the east end of Lake Mývatn, are the most abundant springs in the area.
- **Grænavatn:** A shallow lake, a short distance south of Mývatn, formed as the Younger Laxárhraun lava blocked the Mývatn basin. Grænilækur runs from here into Lake Mývatn.
- **Grænavatn:** A farm in the Mývatn district, mentioned in the Book of Settlements as follows: "Þorkell the Tall came to Iceland as a young man and lived first at Grænavatn..."
- **Grænavatnsbruni:** A lava field south and east of Grænavatn.
- **Hafurshöfði:** A lava headland extending into Lake Mývatn on the east side (*see also Höfði*).
- **Haganes:** A farm. Site of the former local assembly.

- **Háey:** An island and also the tallest pseudo-crater in Lake Mývatn.
- **Helgavogur:** A shallow cove at the northeast end of Mývatn, where tepid spring water (20°–30°C) flows into Mývatn. Previously the local children's swimming lessons took place here. Nearby is a pumping station which pumps raw material from the lake bed to the diatomite factory (*see Kísiliðjan*).
- **Hlíðarfjall:** A rhyolite mountain (771 m) about five km northeast of Lake Mývatn. **H.** was formed during a sub-glacial eruption at the edge of the Krafla caldera (*see also Krafla*). The mountain is easy to climb and affords an excellent view all the way to the sea at Öxarfjörður. There is a walk (about 2 hours) from Reykjahlíð, along Eldá up to the top of the mountain.
- **Hofsstaðir:** A farm at the head of Laxárdalur, best known for the ancient ruin, which was first excavated in 1908. New explorations are now taking place with Icelandic and foreign archaeologists collaborating.
- **Hófur:** A hoof-shaped crater just north of Leirhnjúkur (*see also Leirhnjúkur*). Lava flowed from **H.** during the Mývatn Eruptions 1724–1729.
- **Hrekkur:** A crater just below the explosion crater Víti near Krafla. **H.** was formed in 1975 while drilling for steam for the Krafla power station. The drill hit a steam vein and superheated steam forced its way up to the surface under terrific pressure.
- **Hvannfell:** A steep and narrow tuff ridge (671 m) about ten km east of Lake Mývatn, formed in a sub-glacial eruption.
- **Hverfjall:** Without doubt the most prominent landmark in the mountains surrounding Mývatn, Hverfjall is a circular tephra-cone crater, one of the largest and best known of its type in the world. The crater is thought to have been formed in a single, relatively short-lived but powerful explosive eruption about 2,500 years ago. Its diameter is ca. 1,000 m and it is ca. 140 m deep. The geological history of the area refers to the so-called Hverfjall period, which started about 2,500 years ago and is still going on. Walks link **H.** to Grjótagjá and Dimmuborgir (each walk taking about 1 hour from the edge of the crater).

• **Hverir við Hverarönd:** Hot mud springs east of Námafjall (*see* Námafjall).

• **Höfði:** A lava headland extending into Mývatn on the east side, with many kinds of lava formation. The luxuriant vegetation bears witness to the active cultivation that has taken place here. From the top of **H.** there is a splendid view of nearby inlets and islands.

• **Jarðbaðshólar:** Crater mounds in Bjarnarflag about 4 km east of Mývatn. Lava originating from them stretches as far as the eastern shore of the lake. Underground heat still simmers, and steam escapes from cracks and crevices. Traditionally a popular spot for health-giving steam baths, it has now seen a revival of this custom, and a bathing hut has been built here.

• **Kálfastrandarvogar:** The series of creeks on the eastern side of Mývatn, between Kálfastrandir and Höfði. The Younger Laxárhraun flowed into the pre-existing lake, casting its stamp on the topography of the lake. The interaction between red-hot lava and water formed creeks, ponds and headlands, as well as a myriad of islands and pseudo-craters, lava ridges, ledges and cones, all making their own distinctive mark on the region. The best known lava pillars are Klasar and Kálfastrandarstrípar. There is an easy walk (about 30 min) along the south side of **K.**

• **Kálfaströnd:** A farm – particularly prosperous, according to local history.

• **Kísiliðjan:** A diatomite factory about three km east of Mývatn. Raw material is collected from thick sedimentary layers on the bottom of the lake, consisting mainly of the shells of diatoms. The material is pumped from the lake bed to the factory, where it is cleaned and steam-dried. A steam-powered generating station was built to provide the factory with electricity. Diatomite is used as a filler or filter in various chemical processes. The factory has been in operation since 1967 and the yearly output has reached as much as 30,000 tonnes.

Not only may the *ernal* impurities of the *y* here be cleansed; the *h* is also held to have *et* healing powers, *ch* will remedy human *ments*. Many people *n* the district testify *t* this sweat-bath has *ages* past not only *ted* itching and rashes *also* cured many *ases*...

(Bishop Oddur's Íslandslýsing, end of 16th century)

- **Krafla:** A tuff mountain (818 m) about ten km northeast of Mývatn. It gives its name to Kröfluaskja, a caldera about ten km in diameter which is the central volcano in the ca. 100 km long fissure zone stretching from Bláfjall in the south towards the shores of Öxarfjörður in the north. The volcano was active during the glacial period, and several major eruptions have occurred in this volcanic area since the end of the glacial period about 10,000 years ago (see e.g. Lúdent, Hverfjall and Þrengslaborgir), including twice after Iceland was settled (the Mývatn Eruptions of 1724–1729 and the Krafla Eruptions of 1975–1984). At the centre of the caldera is a powerful geothermal area, which provides energy for the largest steam-driven power station in the country, Kröfluvirkjun.

- **Kráká:** A spring-fed river which rises in the desert highlands south of Mývatn, and flows into Laxá a short distance downstream of its outflow from Lake Mývatn. K. carries with it great quantities of sediment from the wind-swept plateau, a perennial problem for local farmers when it is deposited on their meadows, especially during spring floods (see Framengjar). The sediment is also carried into Laxá, causing increased wear and tear to the hydraulic turbines of the electrical plant at the mouth of the Laxárdalur valley.

- **Landteigar:** A narrow point extending into Mývatn on the east side, opposite Neslanda-tangi. These headlands, formed by the northern edge of the Younger Laxárhraun (see Þrengslaborgir), divide Mývatn into two sections with only a narrow channel between them.

- **Laxá:** One of the largest spring-fed rivers in the country (about 45 m³/sec where it runs into Skjálfandi Bay), L. originates in Mývatn and carries with it from the lake large quantities of nutrients, which are the basis for the rich biology of the river, making L. one of the best fishing rivers in the country. Black Flies are prominent here, being the mainstay of the diet of the Harlequin Duck, the Barrow's Goldeneye and not least the Brown Trout. In the upper reaches only Brown Trout can be found, whereas downstream of the power station there are also Salmon and Charr. The riverbanks are covered in vegetation, as are the hundreds of islets. L. is extremely popular amongst

*About the giantess Krá
In the mountain pastu
of the local Mývatn pe
there was a large lake. K
went thither and upro
a mass of wood; she th
added turf and rocks to
make a massively heav
load, which she dragge
behind her from the lo
down to Mývatn, thro
the whole
district all t
way to Laxá
where it flows
of Lake Mývat.
The load goug
an enormous trench in
which Kráka poured w
saying that a river wo
run through this trenc
as long as folk lived at
Mývatn, and that it w
habitually despoil the
meadows and heathlan
of the local people, wit
no defence from it save
using the stuff of the l
itself; and finally that
river would ruin the
homelands of the regic*

*(From the Folk
of Jón Árn*

fly-fishermen on account of its abundance of fish and natural beauty.

• **Leirhnjúkur:** A small tuff mountain (592 m) about ten km north of Mývatn which is formed of clay-coloured or yellowish tuff, scalded by geothermal heat, and has boiling hot mud springs at its foot. Eruptions have occurred twice in L. in recent centuries (the Mývatn Eruptions of 1724–1729 and the Krafla Eruptions of 1975–1984). The final throes of the Mývatn Eruptions produced a lava flow from L. which destroyed three farms north of Mývatn. There is a posted hike (about 25 min) to L. from a posted car park a short distance above the Kröfluvirkjun power station, as well as a route round the mountain itself (30 min). There is also a short walk from L. to the crater Hófur, another along the Eldá lava flow down towards Reykjahlíð (3–4 hours), and to Námaskarð along Dalfjall (2–2½ hours).

• **Litlaströnd:** A farm in the Mývatn district.

• **Lúdent:** Tephra cone a short distance east of Hverfjall (which is similar but larger). L. is about 600-800 m in diameter and 60–70 m deep. It erupted shortly after the end of the glacial period, about 9,000 years ago, and gives its name to the Lúdent phase (7,000–4,000 BC) in the geological development of the Mývatn region.

• **Lúdentsborgir:** A crater-row named after the tephra cone Lúdent, although it is in fact a northward continuation of the Þrengslaborgir crater-row. This combined crater-row was the source of the Younger Laxárhraun lava flow, following a huge fissure eruption about 2,000 years ago. A day-long walk might be considered (ca. 10 hours) southwards along the crater-row as far as Seljahjallagil, and thence westwards towards either Garður or Grænavatn. Thirsty walkers should note that there is no drinking water to be found on this route.

...ntsborgir in winter.

• **Mikley:** An island in Lake Mývatn. This is the largest island in the lake and was in previous times used for cattle grazing and for haymaking, as were many other islands.

- **Námafjall:** A tuff mountain (485 m) about five km east of Mývatn. There is a view-indicator at the top (which is known as Námakolla). At one time sulphur was extracted for export, the mines being for a long time the property of the Danish Crown. There is a geothermal area here, and the ground is honeycombed with jets of sulphurous steam. On its eastern slopes are numerous hot mud springs, named Hverir við Hverarönd. Extreme caution should be exercised in this area – for the safety of visitors, paths are marked with signposts.
- **Námaskarð:** A mountain pass between Mt. Dalfjall and Mt. Námafjall, through which National Route no.1 connects the Mývatn district with the east of Iceland.
- **Neslandatangi:** A point extending into Lake Mývatn from the northwest, opposite Landteigar. These headlands divide Mývatn into two sections, with only a narrow channel between them. Both points were formed by the northern edge of the Younger Laxárhraun lava field (see Þrengslaborgir). N. has lush vegetation and many ponds.
- **Neslandavík:** A shallow bay in the northeast part of Syðriflói. Until about 1980 swans flocked here in their hundreds during the moulting season; nowadays they have mostly moved over to Ytriflói.
- **Paradís:** A grassy, hollow crater mound with domed top, near the farm Skútustaðir.
- **Reykjahlíð:** A farm in the Mývatn district, with a church standing on the site of a much earlier one. The farm dates from the Settlement; the Book of Settlements says: "Þorsteinn, son of Sigmundur Gnúpa-Bárðarsson, first dwelt at Mývatn. His son was Þorgrímur, father of Arnór at Reykjahlíð." Industry and tourism have brought about an increase in the local population. The farm was destroyed during the Mývatn eruption in 1729, but was rebuilt a short while later. There has been a hotel at R. for several decades.
- **Reynihlíð:** A farm in the Mývatn district. Traditional farming has always been practised here, but in recent decades, its name has been more commonly linked with its hotel and tourist services.

"To the northeast of county is an area cal Námar, where there c sulphur mines. Coun columns of smoke an steam rise up there, v from a great distance. quantities of sulphur transported from here to the nearest harbou Húsavík, and thence Copenhagen to be ref

(From the Travel Jo Eggert Ólafsson and Bjarni latter half of the 18th c

Reykjahlíð

• **Sandvatn:** A shallow lake on the northwest side of Vindbelgjarfjall, just west of Mývatn. It is thought that the predecessor of Lake Mývatn extended south of Vindbelgjarfjall before the Younger Laxárhraun flowed, forming the shore of Lake Mývatn as it is now; a small section of the older lake will have extended north along Vindbelgjarfjall as far as the basin in which **S.** now sits. There are a number of small ponds round **S.** and between them willow-covered heaths alternate with marshy land. The stream Sortulækur runs from **S.** into Laxá river.

• **Seljahjallagil:** A narrow ravine in the Bláfjall mountain range, through which the Younger Laxárhraun ran about 3,800 years ago, characterized by dramatic formations, such as potholes and columnar basalt. For walking routes, see Bláhvammur and Lúdentsborgir.

• **Sellandafjall:** A table mountain (988 m) south of Mývatn. **S.** was formed sub-glacially in the northern section of the volcanic area which straddles the country. The mountain was formed before the last glacial period, as can be seen from its contours (and those of the lava field at its summit), rounded and smoothed by the ice. By comparison, Bláfjall's sharp edges show that it was formed during the latest glacial period. **S.** stands out on its own and can be seen from many directions.

• **Skjólbrekka:** A community hall belonging to the parish of Skútustaðir. In summer, tourist accommodation is available.

• **Skútustaðir:** A farm in the Mývatn district. There has been a church here since ancient times, with a resident minister since 1876. It is said to take its name from Víga-Skúti, a hero and a slayer of men who lived there in the Saga age. **S.** is now the local peoples' meeting place, with a community hall and swimming pool. There is also a natural history research centre, store, coffee shop, hotel and camping area.

• **Skútustaðagígar:** Without doubt the country's best known cluster of pseudo-craters, situated in their dozens on the south side of Lake Mývatn. They were formed during the Younger Laxárhraun lava flow, as were most of the pseudo-craters in the area. The molten lava flowed into the pre-existing lake (Mývatn's forerunner), causing explosions as the resulting steam found an outlet up through the lava. **S.** is a protected area. There are posted hikes through the area (about 30 min).

• **Slútnes:** An island in Lake Mývatn, well known for its vegetation and bird life. The island is covered in birch and Arctic Willow undergrowth. Also notable are Angelica and the characteristic plant of the area, Aaron's Rod or "Queen of Mývatn".

• **Slý:** Marshland, about 2.5 km north of Mývatn, beyond Eldhraun.

• **Stakhólstjörn:** A pond near Skútustaðir on the south coast of Mývatn, it is separated from the lake itself by a low isthmus. The famous Skútustaðagígar are nearby. There is a signposted path round **S.** (about 1 hour's walk).

• **Stóragjá:** A fault fissure containing hot water near Reykjahlíð. From time immemorial a bathing spot for the locals, a pleasure which nowadays they have to share with the world at large.

• **Stöng:** A farm in the Mývatn area. As well as farming, there are amenities for tourists. From **S.** there is a road over to Bárðardalur, which is suitable for all types of road vehicle during the summer months.

• **Svörtuborgir:** A crater-row just north of Hverfjall. There was an eruption here at about the time when Iceland was settled. The lava field from **S.** known as Hverfellsbruni, lies along the foot of Mount Hverfjall.

• **Syðriflói:** Name given to the southern, larger section of Lake Mývatn.

• **Teigasund:** The narrow channel between Neslanda-tangi and Landteigar, **T.** links the two sections of Lake Mývatn, Syðriflói and Ytriflói.

• **Varmholtsgjá:** The lava field south of the village at Reykjahlíð. The walk between Grjótagjá and Stóragjá lies through **V.** as does the circular trip round the area itself (1 hour). This is a sheltered area with lush vegetation and geothermal heat.

• **Villingafjall:** A single tuff mountain (417 m), about three km southeast of Lake Mývatn. **V.** was formed in a sub-glacial eruption. At its foot there is a small wood struggling to survive against erosion.

- **Vindbelgjarfjall:** A single tuff mountain (529 m) to the northwest of Mývatn. V. was formed in a sub-glacial eruption. The mountain is easy to climb, and from its summit there is a particularly good view over Mývatn and the surrounding area. There is a posted hiking path from the farm Vagnbrekka all the way to the summit.
- **Vindbelgur:** A farm in the Mývatn area. Here are the largest pseudo-craters in the area, the so-called Belgjarhöfðar.
- **Víti:** An explosion crater to the northwest of Krafla, about 300 m in diameter. V. was formed in the spring of 1724 in an extremely powerful explosive eruption. A cauldron of boiling hot mud bubbled in the bottom of the crater for more than a century after the eruption, which marked the beginning of the Mývatn Eruptions (1724–1729).
- **Ytriflói:** Name given to the northeastern part of Lake Mývatn, one of the main areas in Iceland where moulting swans congregate during the late summer.
- **Þangbrandspollur:** A pool a short distance from the Skútustaðir farm. The Kristni Saga describes how Þangbrandur the Missionary baptised the local people here.
- **Þrengslaborgir:** A crater-row stretching northwards from Seljahjallagil about five km east of Mývatn; the northern part of it is called Lúdentsborgir. The Younger Laxárhraun flowed from this crater-row in a huge fissure eruption about 2,000 years ago. The lava flowed west down the Laxárdalur valley towards the sea at Skjálfandi Bay, a distance of about 65 km. In its wake many of the best known lava formations round Mývatn were created, such as Dimmuborgir and Kálfastrandarvogar, dozens of islands and a multitude of pseudo-craters. The Younger Laxárhraun completely altered the surroundings round Mývatn and has been particularly instrumental in creating the unique natural beauty of the area. For walking paths *see Lúdentsborgir*.

PLACES OF INTEREST WITHIN REACH OF MÝVATN

Distance from Reykjah

Askja

145 km

A caldera and volcano in the Dyngjufjöll range in the central highlands. Within the caldera is Iceland's deepe lake, Öskjuvatn, formed by a collapse after the eruptio of 1875, when a cloud of smoke and ash from the cra Víti drifted east over the country. Many farmers fled th homes, and the ash fall was instrumental in the emigrati to America from the east of Iceland during the followi years. The landscape hereabouts is bleak and the surroundings are ruggedly dramatic.

Ásbyrgi

95 km

A horseshoe-shaped canyon about 3.5 km in length. A f tale tells how Sleipnir, Odin's eight-legged horse, land here, making a hoof-print in the earth's crust. A gigan waterfall once cascaded down from the top of its innerm cliff, digging at its foot the hollow which now contai a peaceful, tree-ringed pond. It is now established tha Ásbyrgi was formed during a glacier burst thousands of years ago, when the course of the glacial river Jöku á Fjöllum lay further to the west than today.

Dettifoss

70 km

in Jökulsá á Fjöllum is thought to be Europe's most powe waterfall. The surroundings are rugged; steely cliffs, bar sands and rocky ground evoke images of monsters an giants. From the waterfall there is a view along the Jök ravine, the river seeming surprisingly small in compari with its ravine, formed in a massive glacier burst.

Goðafoss

50 km

in Skjálfandafljót is considered one of the country's m beautiful waterfalls. The "Law-Speaker" at the Althing the year 1000, when Christianity was legalized, was a leader of the Pagans, and his decision to convert was instrumental in making the process of Christianizatio peaceful one. Later chronicles tell how he threw the stat of the pagan gods from his temple into this waterfall, which draws its name from the event.

Grenjaðarstaður
40 km

A manor farm of ancient fame, a church and parish in Aðaldalur. At Grenjaðarstaður there is an old turf farmho the basic structure stems from the middle of the 19th century, and it was thought in its time to be the great

*By Route 864 east of Jökulsá á Fjöllum.

and most impressive of all the farms in the district. Grenjaðarstaður farm is now supervised by the National Museum, and the local folk museum is housed here.

Hafragilsfoss

120 km *

A waterfall just downstream from Dettifoss, in one of the most beautiful parts of the canyon. The river has dug its way through an eruption fissure, so that there is a unique cross-section of a crater, exposing the columnar basalt funnel, which spawned the crater at the canyon's rim.

Herðubreiðarlindir

100 km

An oasis of vegetation nestling on the edge of the lava field just west of Jökulsá á Fjöllum, on the route to Askja. Its alpine vegetation and clear spring water form a contrast with the surrounding rough lava and sands. One of the country's most notorious outlaws, Fjalla-Eyvindur, over-wintered here for a time. His lair can still be seen here, one of a few in the Icelandic highlands.

Húsavík

55 km

The Book of Settlements mentions Garðar Svavarsson, a Swedish viking who tried to settle in Iceland. He over-wintered here and built the house which gives the place its name ('House-bay'). In Húsavík there has been a harbour and trading centre from time immemorial. Fishing has always been an important occupation, and the town has recently become increasingly known for whale sightseeing trips. Iceland's first co-operative society, Kaupfélag Þingeyinga, was started in Húsavík in 1882. The old trading-houses still survive and have been restored to their pristine condition. The most remarkable building in Húsavík is without doubt the church, which was designed by Rögnvaldur Ólafsson in 1907. There is a museum with a varied collection of exhibits, and a whaling centre dealing with the history of whales and whale fishing in Iceland.

Vesturdalur

108 km *

A valley in the Jökulsárgljúfur national park. The best known rock formations found here are Hljóðaklettar ('the Echoing Rocks'), the remains of a row of craters. Loose soil has been swept away by successive floods, leaving behind pillars of naked rock containing countless caves.

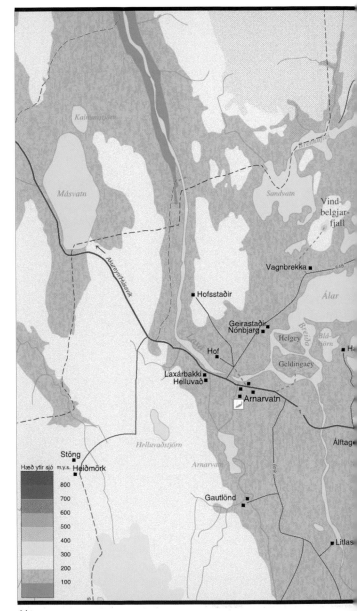

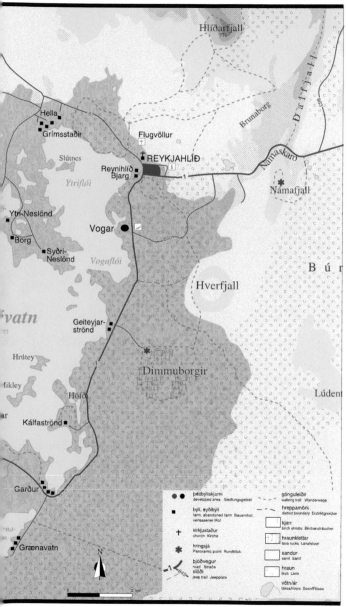

INDEX

INDEX OF NAMES

PICTURE LIST

Sources

Ari Trausti Guðmundsson. 1986. *Íslandseldar. Eldvirkni á Íslandi í 10.000 ár.* Rv., Vaka-Helgafell: 26–37.

Arnþór Garðarsson and Árni Einarsson (editors). 1991. *Náttúra Mývatns.* Rv., Hið íslenska náttúrufræðifélag.

Árni Einarsson. 1988. *Fuglatalningar á Mývatni og Laxá árið 1988.* Mývatn Research Station, report 5. 1989. *Fuglatalningar á Mývatni og Laxá árið 1989.* Mývatn Research Station, report 6.

Árni Magnússon and Páll Vídalín. 1988. *Jarðabók XI.* (2.ed.) Kmh., Hið íslenska fræðafélag: 223–224.

Björn Þorsteinsson. 1964. *Mývatnssveit:Við þjóðveginn.* Rv., Ferðaskrifstofa ríkisins: 17–43.

Bragi Sigurjónsson. *Göngur og réttir V.* (Second edition, revised and extended) Ak., Skjaldborg: 27–166.

Bruun, Daniel. 1987. *Íslenskt þjóðlíf í þúsund ár I.* Translated by Steindór Steindórsson. Rv., Örn og Örlygur hf.: mainly 120–137 and 248–252.

Eggert Ólafsson and Bjarni Pálsson. 1975. *Ferðabók, I–II* (2. ed.) Transl. Steindór Steindórsson. Rv. Örn og Örlygur hf.

Grágás. Lagasafn íslenska þjóðveldisins. 1992. Editors Gunnar Karlsson, Kristján Sveinsson and Mörður Árnason Rv., Mál og Menning.

Íslendingabók. Landnámabók (Early Icelandic texts) 1968. Published by Jakob Benediktsson Rv., Hið íslenska fornritafélag: 282–284.

Íslenskar þjóðsögur og ævintýri I–IV. 1954–1958. New edition. Collected by Jón Árnason. Edited by Árni Böðvarsson and Bjarni Vilhjálmsson Rv., Þjóðsaga

Jónas Jónasson frá Hrafnagili. 1961. *Íslenskir þjóðhættir.* (3.ed.) Revised b Einar Ól. Sveinsson Rv., Ísafoldarprentsmiðja.

Kristján Eldjárn. 1956. *Kuml og haugfé úr heiðnum sið á Íslandi.* Rv., Norðri: 158–161.

Oddur Einarsson. 1971. *Íslandslýsing. Qualiscunque descriptio Islandiae.* Translat by Sveinn Pálsson. Rv., Bókaútgáfa Menningarsjóðs.

Pétur M. Jónasson (ed.). 1979. *Ecology of Eutropic, Subarctic Lake Mývatn and River Laxá.* OIKOS.

Sigurður Jónsson frá Arnarvatni. 1945. *Blessuð sértu sveitin mín.* Rv.

Sigurjón Rist. 1969. *Ice on Mývatn: Hafísinn* (ed. Markús Á. Einarsson). Rv Almenna bókafélagið: 470–478. *Lakes: Náttúra Íslands* (2. ed. Revised and extende Rv., Almenna bókafélagið: 277–302.

Steindór Steindórsson, Guðjón Á Eyjólfsson, Einar Laxness and Þorsteinn Jósepsson. 1980–1984. *Landið þitt Ísland I–VI.* Rv., Örn og Örlygur

Þorleifur Einarsson. 1969. *Climate, sea temperature and polar ice in the Historic Hafísinn* (ed. Markús Á. Einarsson). Rv., Almenna bókafélagið: 389–402.

Þorvaldur Thoroddsen. 1908. *Lýsing Íslands I* Kmh., Hið íslenska bókmenntafélag: 328–329 and 355–357. 1911. *Lýsing Íslands II* Kmh., Hið íslenska bókmenntafélag: 175–187 and 243–246. 1913. *Ferðabók I* Km Hið íslenska fræðafélag: 279–302.